This journal belongs to

———————————————————————

from

___ / ___ / ___

to

___ / ___ / ___

dear UNIVERSE

daily manifestation journal

Introduction

This simple, easy-to-use daily journal provides space for you to manifest your dreams, whatever they may be. Big or small (happy, healthy, wealthy, and/or wise), take 5 minutes each day to visualize and set your intentions.

Create a daily mantra, something to remind yourself to stay focused on your manifestation goals. But not just focused (it's not work!), but a phrase or sentence that will bring you joy just thinking about it.

Give gratitude to the Universe for what you already have. Positive, grateful energy attracts the same energy. By expressing gratitude for what you have, you'll attract more things to be grateful for.

Finally, set your action plan. Even if it's just one small specific step that will get your closer to your manifestation goals. You can do this! The Universe has your back, all you have to do is ask.

Manifestation is a
love letter to the Universe.
ASK, BELIEVE, RECEIVE.

DATE: ___ / ___ / ___

Things I want to manifest:
(visualize each thing, truly feel the joy of receiving it)

1. _____

_____

2. _____

_____

3. _____

_____

Today's affirmation:
(a mantra to repeat throughout the day)

_____

_____

_____

Daily gratitude:

(heartfelt gratitude attracts more abundance)

1. _____

_____

2. _____

_____

3. _____

_____

Action plan:

(something specific to do today to achieve your goals)

_____

_____

_____

_____

DATE: ___ / ___ / ___

Things I want to manifest:
(visualize each thing, truly feel the joy of receiving it)

1. _____

_____

2. _____

_____

3. _____

_____

Today's affirmation:
(a mantra to repeat throughout the day)

_____

_____

_____

Daily gratitude:

(heartfelt gratitude attracts more abundance)

1. _____

_____

2. _____

_____

3. _____

_____

Action plan:

(something specific to do today to achieve your goals)

_____

_____

_____

_____

DATE: ___ / ___ / ___

Things I want to manifest:
(visualize each thing, truly feel the joy of receiving it)

1. _____

_____

2. _____

_____

3. _____

_____

Today's affirmation:
(a mantra to repeat throughout the day)

_____

_____

_____

Daily gratitude:

(heartfelt gratitude attracts more abundance)

1. _____

_____

2. _____

_____

3. _____

_____

Action plan:

(something specific to do today to achieve your goals)

_____

_____

_____

_____

DATE: ___ / ___ / ___

Things I want to manifest:
(visualize each thing, truly feel the joy of receiving it)

1. _____

_____

2. _____

_____

3. _____

_____

Today's affirmation:
(a mantra to repeat throughout the day)

_____

_____

_____

Daily gratitude:

(heartfelt gratitude attracts more abundance)

1. _____

_____

2. _____

_____

3. _____

_____

Action plan:

(something specific to do today to achieve your goals)

_____

_____

_____

_____

DATE: ___ / ___ / ___

Things I want to manifest:
(visualize each thing, truly feel the joy of receiving it)

1. _____

_____

2. _____

_____

3. _____

_____

Today's affirmation:
(a mantra to repeat throughout the day)

_____

_____

_____

Daily gratitude:

(heartfelt gratitude attracts more abundance)

1. _____

_____

2. _____

_____

3. _____

_____

Action plan:

(something specific to do today to achieve your goals)

_____

_____

_____

_____

Things I want to manifest:
(visualize each thing, truly feel the joy of receiving it)

1. _____

_____

2. _____

_____

3. _____

_____

Today's affirmation:
(a mantra to repeat throughout the day)

_____

_____

_____

Daily gratitude:

(heartfelt gratitude attracts more abundance)

1. _____

_____

2. _____

_____

3. _____

_____

Action plan:

(something specific to do today to achieve your goals)

_____

_____

_____

_____

Things I want to manifest:

(visualize each thing, truly feel the joy of receiving it)

1. _____

_____

2. _____

_____

3. _____

_____

Today's affirmation:

(a mantra to repeat throughout the day)

_____

_____

_____

Daily gratitude:

(heartfelt gratitude attracts more abundance)

1. _____

_____

2. _____

_____

3. _____

_____

Action plan:

(something specific to do today to achieve your goals)

_____

_____

_____

_____

DATE: ___ / ___ / ___

Things I want to manifest:
(visualize each thing, truly feel the joy of receiving it)

1. _____

_____

2. _____

_____

3. _____

_____

Today's affirmation:
(a mantra to repeat throughout the day)

_____

_____

_____

Daily gratitude:

(heartfelt gratitude attracts more abundance)

1. _____

_____

2. _____

_____

3. _____

_____

Action plan:

(something specific to do today to achieve your goals)

_____

_____

_____

_____

DATE: ___ / ___ / ___

Things I want to manifest:
(visualize each thing, truly feel the joy of receiving it)

1. _____

_____

2. _____

_____

3. _____

_____

Today's affirmation:
(a mantra to repeat throughout the day)

_____

_____

_____

Daily gratitude:

(heartfelt gratitude attracts more abundance)

1. _____

_____

2. _____

_____

3. _____

_____

Action plan:

(something specific to do today to achieve your goals)

_____

_____

_____

_____

DATE: ___ / ___ / ___

Things I want to manifest:
(visualize each thing, truly feel the joy of receiving it)

1. _____

_____

2. _____

_____

3. _____

_____

Today's affirmation:
(a mantra to repeat throughout the day)

_____

_____

_____

Daily gratitude:

(heartfelt gratitude attracts more abundance)

1. _____

_____

2. _____

_____

3. _____

_____

Action plan:

(something specific to do today to achieve your goals)

_____

_____

_____

_____

Things I want to manifest:

(visualize each thing, truly feel the joy of receiving it)

1. _____

_____

2. _____

_____

3. _____

_____

Today's affirmation:

(a mantra to repeat throughout the day)

_____

_____

_____

Daily gratitude:
(heartfelt gratitude attracts more abundance)

1. _____

_____

2. _____

_____

3. _____

_____

Action plan:
(something specific to do today to achieve your goals)

_____

_____

_____

_____

DATE: ___ / ___ / ___

Things I want to manifest:
(visualize each thing, truly feel the joy of receiving it)

1. _____

_____

2. _____

_____

3. _____

_____

Today's affirmation:
(a mantra to repeat throughout the day)

_____

_____

_____

Daily gratitude:
(heartfelt gratitude attracts more abundance)

1. _____

_____

2. _____

_____

3. _____

_____

Action plan:
(something specific to do today to achieve your goals)

_____

_____

_____

_____

Things I want to manifest:
(visualize each thing, truly feel the joy of receiving it)

1. _____

_____

2. _____

_____

3. _____

_____

Today's affirmation:
(a mantra to repeat throughout the day)

_____

_____

_____

Daily gratitude:

(heartfelt gratitude attracts more abundance)

1. _____

_____

2. _____

_____

3. _____

_____

Action plan:

(something specific to do today to achieve your goals)

_____

_____

_____

_____

Things I want to manifest:

(visualize each thing, truly feel the joy of receiving it)

1. _____

_____

2. _____

_____

3. _____

_____

Today's affirmation:

(a mantra to repeat throughout the day)

_____

_____

_____

Daily gratitude:
(heartfelt gratitude attracts more abundance)

1. _____

_____

2. _____

_____

3. _____

_____

Action plan:
(something specific to do today to achieve your goals)

_____

_____

_____

_____

DATE: ___ / ___ / ___

Things I want to manifest:
(visualize each thing, truly feel the joy of receiving it)

1. _____

_____

2. _____

_____

3. _____

_____

Today's affirmation:
(a mantra to repeat throughout the day)

_____

_____

_____

Daily gratitude:
(heartfelt gratitude attracts more abundance)

1. _____

_____

2. _____

_____

3. _____

_____

Action plan:
(something specific to do today to achieve your goals)

_____

_____

_____

_____

DATE: ___ / ___ / ___

Things I want to manifest:
(visualize each thing, truly feel the joy of receiving it)

1. _____

_____

2. _____

_____

3. _____

_____

Today's affirmation:
(a mantra to repeat throughout the day)

_____

_____

_____

Daily gratitude:

(heartfelt gratitude attracts more abundance)

1. _____

_____

2. _____

_____

3. _____

_____

Action plan:

(something specific to do today to achieve your goals)

_____

_____

_____

_____

DATE: ___ / ___ / ___

Things I want to manifest:
(visualize each thing, truly feel the joy of receiving it)

1. _____

_____

2. _____

_____

3. _____

_____

Today's affirmation:
(a mantra to repeat throughout the day)

_____

_____

_____

Daily gratitude:
(heartfelt gratitude attracts more abundance)

1. _____

_____

2. _____

_____

3. _____

_____

Action plan:
(something specific to do today to achieve your goals)

_____

_____

_____

_____

DATE: ___ / ___ / ___

Things I want to manifest:
(visualize each thing, truly feel the joy of receiving it)

1. _____

_____

2. _____

_____

3. _____

_____

Today's affirmation:
(a mantra to repeat throughout the day)

_____

_____

_____

Daily gratitude:

(heartfelt gratitude attracts more abundance)

1. _____

_____

2. _____

_____

3. _____

_____

Action plan:

(something specific to do today to achieve your goals)

_____

_____

_____

_____

DATE: ___ / ___ / ___

Things I want to manifest:
(visualize each thing, truly feel the joy of receiving it)

1. _____

_____

2. _____

_____

3. _____

_____

Today's affirmation:
(a mantra to repeat throughout the day)

_____

_____

_____

Daily gratitude:

(heartfelt gratitude attracts more abundance)

1. _____

_____

2. _____

_____

3. _____

_____

Action plan:

(something specific to do today to achieve your goals)

_____

_____

_____

_____

DATE: ___ / ___ / ___

Things I want to manifest:
(visualize each thing, truly feel the joy of receiving it)

1. _____

_____

2. _____

_____

3. _____

_____

Today's affirmation:
(a mantra to repeat throughout the day)

_____

_____

_____

Daily gratitude:

(heartfelt gratitude attracts more abundance)

1. _____

_____

2. _____

_____

3. _____

_____

Action plan:

(something specific to do today to achieve your goals)

_____

_____

_____

_____

DATE: ___ / ___ / ___

Things I want to manifest:
(visualize each thing, truly feel the joy of receiving it)

1. _____

_____

2. _____

_____

3. _____

_____

Today's affirmation:
(a mantra to repeat throughout the day)

_____

_____

_____

Daily gratitude:

(heartfelt gratitude attracts more abundance)

1. _____

_____

2. _____

_____

3. _____

_____

Action plan:

(something specific to do today to achieve your goals)

_____

_____

_____

_____

DATE: ___ / ___ / ___

Things I want to manifest:

(visualize each thing, truly feel the joy of receiving it)

1. _____

_____

2. _____

_____

3. _____

_____

Today's affirmation:

(a mantra to repeat throughout the day)

_____

_____

_____

Daily gratitude:

(heartfelt gratitude attracts more abundance)

1. _____

_____

2. _____

_____

3. _____

_____

Action plan:

(something specific to do today to achieve your goals)

_____

_____

_____

_____

DATE: ___ / ___ / ___

Things I want to manifest:
(visualize each thing, truly feel the joy of receiving it)

1. _____

_____

2. _____

_____

3. _____

_____

Today's affirmation:
(a mantra to repeat throughout the day)

_____

_____

_____

Daily gratitude:
(heartfelt gratitude attracts more abundance)

1. _____

_____

2. _____

_____

3. _____

_____

Action plan:
(something specific to do today to achieve your goals)

_____

_____

_____

_____

DATE: ___ / ___ / ___

Things I want to manifest:
(visualize each thing, truly feel the joy of receiving it)

1. _____

_____

2. _____

_____

3. _____

_____

Today's affirmation:
(a mantra to repeat throughout the day)

_____

_____

_____

Daily gratitude:

(heartfelt gratitude attracts more abundance)

1. _____

_____

2. _____

_____

3. _____

_____

Action plan:

(something specific to do today to achieve your goals)

_____

_____

_____

_____

Things I want to manifest:

(visualize each thing, truly feel the joy of receiving it)

1. _____

_____

2. _____

_____

3. _____

_____

Today's affirmation:

(a mantra to repeat throughout the day)

_____

_____

_____

Daily gratitude:

(heartfelt gratitude attracts more abundance)

1. _____

_____

2. _____

_____

3. _____

_____

Action plan:

(something specific to do today to achieve your goals)

_____

_____

_____

_____

DATE: ___ / ___ / ___

Things I want to manifest:
(visualize each thing, truly feel the joy of receiving it)

1. _____

_____

2. _____

_____

3. _____

_____

Today's affirmation:
(a mantra to repeat throughout the day)

_____

_____

_____

Daily gratitude:

(heartfelt gratitude attracts more abundance)

1. _____

_____

2. _____

_____

3. _____

_____

Action plan:

(something specific to do today to achieve your goals)

_____

_____

_____

_____

DATE: ___ / ___ / ___

Things I want to manifest:
(visualize each thing, truly feel the joy of receiving it)

1. _____

_____

2. _____

_____

3. _____

_____

Today's affirmation:
(a mantra to repeat throughout the day)

_____

_____

_____

Daily gratitude:

(heartfelt gratitude attracts more abundance)

1. _____

_____

2. _____

_____

3. _____

_____

Action plan:

(something specific to do today to achieve your goals)

_____

_____

_____

_____

DATE: ___ / ___ / ___

Things I want to manifest:
(visualize each thing, truly feel the joy of receiving it)

1. _____

_____

2. _____

_____

3. _____

_____

Today's affirmation:
(a mantra to repeat throughout the day)

_____

_____

_____

Daily gratitude:

(heartfelt gratitude attracts more abundance)

1. _____

_____

2. _____

_____

3. _____

_____

Action plan:

(something specific to do today to achieve your goals)

_____

_____

_____

_____

DATE: ___ / ___ / ___

Things I want to manifest:
(visualize each thing, truly feel the joy of receiving it)

1. _____

_____

2. _____

_____

3. _____

_____

Today's affirmation:
(a mantra to repeat throughout the day)

_____

_____

_____

Daily gratitude:
(heartfelt gratitude attracts more abundance)

1. _____

_____

2. _____

_____

3. _____

_____

Action plan:
(something specific to do today to achieve your goals)

_____

_____

_____

_____

DATE: ___ / ___ / ___

Things I want to manifest:
(visualize each thing, truly feel the joy of receiving it)

1. _____

_____

2. _____

_____

3. _____

_____

Today's affirmation:
(a mantra to repeat throughout the day)

_____

_____

_____

Daily gratitude:

(heartfelt gratitude attracts more abundance)

1. _____

_____

2. _____

_____

3. _____

_____

Action plan:

(something specific to do today to achieve your goals)

_____

_____

_____

_____

DATE: ___ / ___ / ___

Things I want to manifest:
(visualize each thing, truly feel the joy of receiving it)

1. _____

_____

2. _____

_____

3. _____

_____

Today's affirmation:
(a mantra to repeat throughout the day)

_____

_____

_____

Daily gratitude:
(heartfelt gratitude attracts more abundance)

1. _____

_____

2. _____

_____

3. _____

_____

Action plan:
(something specific to do today to achieve your goals)

_____

_____

_____

_____

Things I want to manifest:

(visualize each thing, truly feel the joy of receiving it)

1. _____

_____

2. _____

_____

3. _____

_____

Today's affirmation:

(a mantra to repeat throughout the day)

_____

_____

_____

Daily gratitude:

(heartfelt gratitude attracts more abundance)

1. _____

_____

2. _____

_____

3. _____

_____

Action plan:

(something specific to do today to achieve your goals)

_____

_____

_____

_____

DATE: ___ / ___ / ___

Things I want to manifest:
(visualize each thing, truly feel the joy of receiving it)

1. _____

_____

2. _____

_____

3. _____

_____

Today's affirmation:
(a mantra to repeat throughout the day)

_____

_____

_____

Daily gratitude:

(heartfelt gratitude attracts more abundance)

1. _____

_____

2. _____

_____

3. _____

_____

Action plan:

(something specific to do today to achieve your goals)

_____

_____

_____

_____

DATE: ___ / ___ / ___

Things I want to manifest:
(visualize each thing, truly feel the joy of receiving it)

1. _____

_____

2. _____

_____

3. _____

_____

Today's affirmation:
(a mantra to repeat throughout the day)

_____

_____

_____

Daily gratitude:

(heartfelt gratitude attracts more abundance)

1. _____

_____

2. _____

_____

3. _____

_____

Action plan:

(something specific to do today to achieve your goals)

_____

_____

_____

_____

DATE: ___ / ___ / ___

Things I want to manifest:
(visualize each thing, truly feel the joy of receiving it)

1. _____

_____

2. _____

_____

3. _____

_____

Today's affirmation:
(a mantra to repeat throughout the day)

_____

_____

_____

Daily gratitude:

(heartfelt gratitude attracts more abundance)

1. _____

_____

2. _____

_____

3. _____

_____

Action plan:

(something specific to do today to achieve your goals)

_____

_____

_____

_____

DATE: ___ / ___ / ___

Things I want to manifest:
(visualize each thing, truly feel the joy of receiving it)

1. _____

_____

2. _____

_____

3. _____

_____

Today's affirmation:
(a mantra to repeat throughout the day)

_____

_____

_____

Daily gratitude:

(heartfelt gratitude attracts more abundance)

1. _____

_____

2. _____

_____

3. _____

_____

Action plan:

(something specific to do today to achieve your goals)

_____

_____

_____

_____

DATE: ___ / ___ / ___

Things I want to manifest:
(visualize each thing, truly feel the joy of receiving it)

1. _____

_____

2. _____

_____

3. _____

_____

Today's affirmation:
(a mantra to repeat throughout the day)

_____

_____

_____

Daily gratitude:

(heartfelt gratitude attracts more abundance)

1. _____

_____

2. _____

_____

3. _____

_____

Action plan:

(something specific to do today to achieve your goals)

_____

_____

_____

_____

DATE: ___ / ___ / ___

Things I want to manifest:
(visualize each thing, truly feel the joy of receiving it)

1. _____

_____

2. _____

_____

3. _____

_____

Today's affirmation:
(a mantra to repeat throughout the day)

_____

_____

_____

Daily gratitude:

(heartfelt gratitude attracts more abundance)

1. _____

_____

2. _____

_____

3. _____

_____

Action plan:

(something specific to do today to achieve your goals)

_____

_____

_____

_____

DATE: ___ / ___ / ___

Things I want to manifest:
(visualize each thing, truly feel the joy of receiving it)

1. _____

_____

2. _____

_____

3. _____

_____

Today's affirmation:
(a mantra to repeat throughout the day)

_____

_____

_____

Daily gratitude:

(heartfelt gratitude attracts more abundance)

1. _____

_____

2. _____

_____

3. _____

_____

Action plan:

(something specific to do today to achieve your goals)

_____

_____

_____

_____

DATE: ___ / ___ / ___

Things I want to manifest:
(visualize each thing, truly feel the joy of receiving it)

1. _____

_____

2. _____

_____

3. _____

_____

Today's affirmation:
(a mantra to repeat throughout the day)

_____

_____

_____

Daily gratitude:

(heartfelt gratitude attracts more abundance)

1. _____

_____

2. _____

_____

3. _____

_____

Action plan:

(something specific to do today to achieve your goals)

_____

_____

_____

_____

DATE: ___ / ___ / ___

Things I want to manifest:
(visualize each thing, truly feel the joy of receiving it)

1. _____

_____

2. _____

_____

3. _____

_____

Today's affirmation:
(a mantra to repeat throughout the day)

_____

_____

_____

Daily gratitude:

(heartfelt gratitude attracts more abundance)

1. _____

_____

2. _____

_____

3. _____

_____

Action plan:

(something specific to do today to achieve your goals)

_____

_____

_____

_____

DATE: ___ / ___ / ___

Things I want to manifest:
(visualize each thing, truly feel the joy of receiving it)

1. _____

_____

2. _____

_____

3. _____

_____

Today's affirmation:
(a mantra to repeat throughout the day)

_____

_____

_____

Daily gratitude:

(heartfelt gratitude attracts more abundance)

1. _____

_____

2. _____

_____

3. _____

_____

Action plan:

(something specific to do today to achieve your goals)

_____

_____

_____

_____

DATE: ___ / ___ / ___

Things I want to manifest:
(visualize each thing, truly feel the joy of receiving it)

1. _____

_____

2. _____

_____

3. _____

_____

Today's affirmation:
(a mantra to repeat throughout the day)

_____

_____

_____

Daily gratitude:

(heartfelt gratitude attracts more abundance)

1. _____

_____

2. _____

_____

3. _____

_____

Action plan:

(something specific to do today to achieve your goals)

_____

_____

_____

_____

DATE: ___ / ___ / ___

Things I want to manifest:
(visualize each thing, truly feel the joy of receiving it)

1. _____

_____

2. _____

_____

3. _____

_____

Today's affirmation:
(a mantra to repeat throughout the day)

_____

_____

_____

Daily gratitude:

(heartfelt gratitude attracts more abundance)

1. _____

_____

2. _____

_____

3. _____

_____

Action plan:

(something specific to do today to achieve your goals)

_____

_____

_____

_____

DATE: ___ / ___ / ___

Things I want to manifest:
(visualize each thing, truly feel the joy of receiving it)

1. _____

_____

2. _____

_____

3. _____

_____

Today's affirmation:
(a mantra to repeat throughout the day)

_____

_____

_____

Daily gratitude:

(heartfelt gratitude attracts more abundance)

1. _____

_____

2. _____

_____

3. _____

_____

Action plan:

(something specific to do today to achieve your goals)

_____

_____

_____

_____

DATE: ___ / ___ / ___

Things I want to manifest:
(visualize each thing, truly feel the joy of receiving it)

1. _____

_____

2. _____

_____

3. _____

_____

Today's affirmation:
(a mantra to repeat throughout the day)

_____

_____

_____

Daily gratitude:

(heartfelt gratitude attracts more abundance)

1. _____

_____

2. _____

_____

3. _____

_____

Action plan:

(something specific to do today to achieve your goals)

_____

_____

_____

_____

DATE: ___ / ___ / ___

Things I want to manifest:
(visualize each thing, truly feel the joy of receiving it)

1. _____

_____

2. _____

_____

3. _____

_____

Today's affirmation:
(a mantra to repeat throughout the day)

_____

_____

_____

Daily gratitude:

(heartfelt gratitude attracts more abundance)

1. _____

_____

2. _____

_____

3. _____

_____

Action plan:

(something specific to do today to achieve your goals)

_____

_____

_____

_____

DATE: ___ / ___ / ___

Things I want to manifest:
(visualize each thing, truly feel the joy of receiving it)

1. _____

_____

2. _____

_____

3. _____

_____

Today's affirmation:
(a mantra to repeat throughout the day)

_____

_____

_____

Daily gratitude:

(heartfelt gratitude attracts more abundance)

1. _____

_____

2. _____

_____

3. _____

_____

Action plan:

(something specific to do today to achieve your goals)

_____

_____

_____

_____

DATE: ___ / ___ / ___

Things I want to manifest:
(visualize each thing, truly feel the joy of receiving it)

1. _____

_____

2. _____

_____

3. _____

_____

Today's affirmation:
(a mantra to repeat throughout the day)

_____

_____

_____

Daily gratitude:

(heartfelt gratitude attracts more abundance)

1. _____

_____

2. _____

_____

3. _____

_____

Action plan:

(something specific to do today to achieve your goals)

_____

_____

_____

_____

DATE: ___ / ___ / ___

Things I want to manifest:
(visualize each thing, truly feel the joy of receiving it)

1. _____

_____

2. _____

_____

3. _____

_____

Today's affirmation:
(a mantra to repeat throughout the day)

_____

_____

_____

Daily gratitude:

(heartfelt gratitude attracts more abundance)

1. _____

_____

2. _____

_____

3. _____

_____

Action plan:

(something specific to do today to achieve your goals)

_____

_____

_____

_____

DATE: ___ / ___ / ___

Things I want to manifest:
(visualize each thing, truly feel the joy of receiving it)

1. _____

_____

2. _____

_____

3. _____

_____

Today's affirmation:
(a mantra to repeat throughout the day)

_____

_____

_____

Daily gratitude:

(heartfelt gratitude attracts more abundance)

1. _____

_____

2. _____

_____

3. _____

_____

Action plan:

(something specific to do today to achieve your goals)

_____

_____

_____

_____

DATE: ___ / ___ / ___

Things I want to manifest:
(visualize each thing, truly feel the joy of receiving it)

1. _____

_____

2. _____

_____

3. _____

_____

Today's affirmation:
(a mantra to repeat throughout the day)

_____

_____

_____

Daily gratitude:

(heartfelt gratitude attracts more abundance)

1. _____

_____

2. _____

_____

3. _____

_____

Action plan:

(something specific to do today to achieve your goals)

_____

_____

_____

_____

DATE: ___ / ___ / ___

Things I want to manifest:
(visualize each thing, truly feel the joy of receiving it)

1. _____

_____

2. _____

_____

3. _____

_____

Today's affirmation:
(a mantra to repeat throughout the day)

_____

_____

_____

Daily gratitude:

(heartfelt gratitude attracts more abundance)

1. _____

_____

2. _____

_____

3. _____

_____

Action plan:

(something specific to do today to achieve your goals)

_____

_____

_____

_____

DATE: ___ / ___ / ___

Things I want to manifest:
(visualize each thing, truly feel the joy of receiving it)

1. _____

_____

2. _____

_____

3. _____

_____

Today's affirmation:
(a mantra to repeat throughout the day)

_____

_____

_____

Daily gratitude:

(heartfelt gratitude attracts more abundance)

1. _____

_____

2. _____

_____

3. _____

_____

Action plan:

(something specific to do today to achieve your goals)

_____

_____

_____

_____

DATE: ___ / ___ / ___

Things I want to manifest:
(visualize each thing, truly feel the joy of receiving it)

1. _____

_____

2. _____

_____

3. _____

_____

Today's affirmation:
(a mantra to repeat throughout the day)

_____

_____

_____

Daily gratitude:

(heartfelt gratitude attracts more abundance)

1. _____

_____

2. _____

_____

3. _____

_____

Action plan:

(something specific to do today to achieve your goals)

_____

_____

_____

_____

DATE: ___ / ___ / ___

Things I want to manifest:
(visualize each thing, truly feel the joy of receiving it)

1. _____

_____

2. _____

_____

3. _____

_____

Today's affirmation:
(a mantra to repeat throughout the day)

_____

_____

_____

Daily gratitude:

(heartfelt gratitude attracts more abundance)

1. _____

_____

2. _____

_____

3. _____

_____

Action plan:

(something specific to do today to achieve your goals)

_____

_____

_____

_____

DATE: ___ / ___ / ___

Things I want to manifest:
(visualize each thing, truly feel the joy of receiving it)

1. _____

_____

2. _____

_____

3. _____

_____

Today's affirmation:
(a mantra to repeat throughout the day)

_____

_____

_____

Daily gratitude:

(heartfelt gratitude attracts more abundance)

1. _____

_____

2. _____

_____

3. _____

_____

Action plan:

(something specific to do today to achieve your goals)

_____

_____

_____

_____

DATE: ___ / ___ / ___

Things I want to manifest:
(visualize each thing, truly feel the joy of receiving it)

1. _____

_____

2. _____

_____

3. _____

_____

Today's affirmation:
(a mantra to repeat throughout the day)

_____

_____

_____

Daily gratitude:

(heartfelt gratitude attracts more abundance)

1. _____

_____

2. _____

_____

3. _____

_____

Action plan:

(something specific to do today to achieve your goals)

_____

_____

_____

_____

DATE: ___ / ___ / ___

Things I want to manifest:
(visualize each thing, truly feel the joy of receiving it)

1. _____

_____

2. _____

_____

3. _____

_____

Today's affirmation:
(a mantra to repeat throughout the day)

_____

_____

_____

Daily gratitude:

(heartfelt gratitude attracts more abundance)

1. _____

_____

2. _____

_____

3. _____

_____

Action plan:

(something specific to do today to achieve your goals)

_____

_____

_____

_____

DATE: ___ / ___ / ___

Things I want to manifest:
(visualize each thing, truly feel the joy of receiving it)

1. _____

_____

2. _____

_____

3. _____

_____

Today's affirmation:
(a mantra to repeat throughout the day)

_____

_____

_____

Daily gratitude:

(heartfelt gratitude attracts more abundance)

1. _____

_____

2. _____

_____

3. _____

_____

Action plan:

(something specific to do today to achieve your goals)

_____

_____

_____

_____

BLUE BIRD BOOKS

Daily Gratitude Journals

SQUEEZE THE DAY

GROW YOUR OWN WAY

BEACH DAY EVERY DAY

RESTING BEACH FACE

PRETTY GRATEFUL
(Champagne, Eggshell Blue, Rose Gold)

Christian Gratitude Journals

GOD, GRATITUDE, & GRACE

OH GIVE THANKS UNTO THE LORD

Daily Journals

DEAR UNIVERSE
Daily Manifestation Journal

WHAT DO I NEED TO KNOW?
(Amethyst & Sage, Sand & Sea)
Daily Tarot Card Journal

Amazon | amazon.com – Barnes & Noble | bn.com